WHAT IS GOD LIKE?

WHAT IS
GOD LIKE?

ROBBIE TRENT

Illustrations by
JOSEPHINE HASKELL

HARPER & BROTHERS, PUBLISHERS
New York

Library of Congress catalog card number: 53-5453

WHAT IS GOD LIKE?

Philip lay on the shore and splashed the water with his bare feet.
His fingers combed the sand until they found a small hard object.
He examined it closely. "Father," he called,
"Why does this one have five rings? On some there are seven."

His father finished putting the net back in the water.
Then he came over and sat down by his son.
"Your name means lover of horses," he teased Philip.
"I should have given you one that means asker of questions."

He took the tiny shell in his hand.
With one finger he counted the spirals.
"God has given you eyes to see and a mind to think.
I am glad you are using both of them.

"The miracle of form and pattern I cannot explain.
Even among small creatures each one is different.
Such design reminds me of wise words spoken long ago,
Stand still, and consider the wondrous works of God."

Philip and his father lived in the town of Bethsaida
On the shore of the blue Lake of Gennesaret,
In the Roman province of Galilee
In the land of Palestine.

Even as a small boy Philip had always been asking questions,
And his father had tried to answer each one.
"Who made it?" Philip had asked one day.
And he pointed to the sun high in the sky.

"God," his father had replied.
"God made two great lights;
The greater light to rule the day,
And the lesser light to rule the night."

As Philip grew bigger, he asked bigger questions.
In the orchard one day he sniffed the smell of ripe fruit
And bit into a date sweet like honey. Then he asked,
"Why do date palms always grow from date seed?"

His father took a stone, and broke open the shell of a seed.
Philip dug out the white kernel inside.
"In each seed," his father explained,
"God has put the beginnings of a plant of that same kind.

"God said, Let the earth bring forth grass,
The herb yielding seed,
And the fruit tree yielding fruit after its kind,
Whose seed is in itself, upon the earth: and it was so."

Now that Philip was nine years old,
His questions were even more thoughtful.
Down by the lake one day he asked a new one.
"Father, what is God like?"

His father did not answer just then.
Instead, he pointed to a gull flying high in the blue sky,
Then to a great fish swimming in the blue waters.
At last he spoke.

"God is the Creator of life.
God created great whales,
And every living creature that moveth, . . .
And every winged fowl."

Philip nodded his head.
"Since I was small, I have known that God is the Creator.
Now I want to know more." He was silent for a moment.
Then he whispered, "I wish I could see God."

His father's words came slowly.
"Once long ago there lived a man whose name was Moses.
He led his people from the slavery of Egypt to a new land,
And he talked much with God.

"One day Moses went into the Tent of Meeting.
He went seeking the will of God for himself and for his people.
And the Lord spake unto Moses face to face,
As a man speaketh unto his friend."

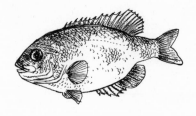

Philip looked hard at his father.
"Did Moses really see God?" he asked.
His father shook his head.
"I do not know," he said.

He bent forward and dipped his hand in the clear water.
Philip watched him lift it high and open his fingers.
He saw the drops sparkle in the sunlight as they fell to earth.
Then his father spoke.

"God is holy and perfect, my son.
Who shall ascend into the hill of the Lord?
Or who shall stand in his holy place?
He that hath clean hands, and a pure heart."

The boy looked down at his fingers sticky with sand.
He rubbed them together.
Then across his forehead.
They left spots of brown that matched his soiled hands.

His father moved nearer Philip.
He put his arm around his son's shoulders, and drew him close.
Together they looked at the faraway hills across the water.
When his father spoke, his voice was gentle.

"God understands all about us.
The Lord seeth not as man seeth;
For man looketh on the outward appearance,
But the Lord looketh on the heart."

Philip dug his heel back and forth into the ground.
He shifted his body on the sand,
And drew a long breath.
His father went on.

"God knows all we do, all we say and think.
He knows all we are and all we want to be.
With mercy and goodness he seeks to bind us to righteousness.
So did the old prophet tell us long ago.

"Thus saith the Lord, . . .
I have loved thee with an everlasting love:
Therefore with loving kindness
Have I drawn thee."

Still the boy's eyes were anxious.
Elbows on his knees,
He rested his chin in his hands.
His lips parted to ask another question.

Then Philip saw that his father was not looking at him.
His eyes were lifted to the heavens.
He was speaking to Someone,
And his words were an old prayer.

"Thou, Lord, art good,
And ready to forgive; . . .
Create in me a clean heart, O God;
And renew a right spirit within me."

Another day a storm came. Thunder crashed.
A great wind shook the trees on the mountain tops,
And lightning cut jagged patterns in the dark clouds.
"Aren't you ever afraid, Father?" Philip asked.

The father took his son's hand and held it tight.
His voice was gentle, yet strong.
"Yes, my son, often there is fear in my heart,
But that is when I have forgotten God's care.

"God is our refuge and strength,
A very present help in trouble.
Therefore will not we fear, though the earth be removed,
And though the mountains be carried into the midst of the sea."

The rain was gentle now.
Father and son watched the drops falling on the dry ground.
Soon they smelled the freshness of earth washed clean.
They sniffed the odor of hyacinth buds half open.

Philip saw the petals of a purple sword lily uncurl.
He counted three colors of crocus—pink, and lavender, and yellow.
With one finger he touched a wet leaf on an oleander bush.
His father spoke of the rain.

"God . . . causeth it to come,
Whether for correction,
Or for his land,
Or for mercy."

As quickly as they had gathered, the clouds sailed away.
Again Philip saw the sun shining on the earth.
He saw his own face reflected in a clear pool of water.
In the same pool he saw a tiny rainbow.

His ears caught, far away, the croaking of a frog.
Then, near at hand, he heard another sound—
The birds were chirping.
His father heard too.

"God has planned for the little creatures," his father said.
"He has provided leafy branches for their homes.
The trees of the Lord are full of sap . . .
Where the birds make their nests."

Together Philip and his father watched the mother bird.
They saw her push a young bird from the nest.
When it was about to fall, she caught it on her wing,
And carried it back up to the nest.

"Is she teaching the young bird to fly?" the boy asked.
"Yes," his father answered. "And so God teaches his people.
Daily he pushes them into new situations that test their strength.
Ever he stands by to help when that strength fails.

"Wherever you go, my son,
Remember this.
The eternal God is thy refuge,
And underneath are the everlasting arms."

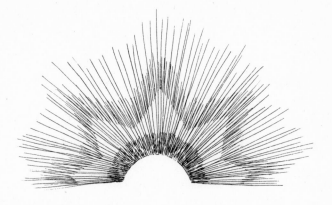

Sunset came. The crimson glow over Mount Tabor turned to pink,
The pink faded into silver, and the silver into gray twilight.
Then darkness came. It was night.
Philip and his father watched the moon climb high in the sky.

His father spoke of tides and seasons,
And of how the moon has strange power over them.
He told of God's laws which govern the day and the night.
Then, as if to himself, he repeated an old poem.

"O Lord our Lord, how excellent is thy name in all the earth! . . .
When I consider thy heavens, the work of thy fingers,
The moon and the stars, which thou hast ordained;
What is man, that thou art mindful of him?"

It was time to sleep.
Again clouds had filled the sky.
Philip saw strange objects as he lay in the darkness.
He pressed his lips tight together to keep from crying out.

Far away he heard the hoarse cry of a jackal.
Then, near at hand, his ears caught a light step—and his father's voice.
"God has not left us alone," his father reminded him.
"He is near us in the night as in the day.

"Blessed be the name of God . . .
He knoweth what is in the darkness,
Thou shalt lie down,
And none shall make thee afraid."

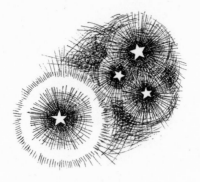

High in the heavens
The dark clouds moved away.
The stars came out,
And their light was soft and shining.

Philip pointed out the North Star,
And his father spoke of its steady light.
He told how it guided the sailors at sea.
"You can count on the North Star," he said.

"O give thanks unto the Lord . . .
To him that made great lights.
He telleth the number of the stars;
He calleth them all by their names."

Now the moon was shining again,
And its light pushed the shadows from the room.
Instead of threatening dark shapes,
Philip saw a familiar stool and his own chair.

His hand in his father's,
Philip listened to talk of planets and stars,
Each one separate,
Each one an orderly part of God's universe.

"God is the Maker of order,"
His father said.
"The heavens declare the glory of God;
And the firmament sheweth his handywork."

Years passed. As Philip grew older,
He learned from his teachers,
And he learned from his father.
And he kept on asking questions.

One day he watched his father count out money for Roman taxes.
"Why must a foreign national rule our land?" he asked sadly.
"Why does God prosper the heathen?"
His father waited a moment before he replied.

"I cannot answer your question, my son.
But one thing I know. God is just.
The Lord is righteous in all his ways,
And holy in all his works."

Another day Philip watched soldiers marching through the town.
"Soldiers mean war," Philip told his father.
"Why does God let men kill each other?
Why does he allow them to lay waste cities and countries?"

"The evil deeds of men bring war,"
His father replied, "No evil is of God."
The slow tramp of feet died away,
And again Philip's father spoke.

"Some day, some great, good day,
When men have learned to walk in right ways,
Nation shall not lift up sword against nation,
Neither shall they learn war any more."

Philip grew tall. At last he was a young man.
He tried not to notice that age had bowed his father's shoulders.
On days when the sun was shining, they walked to the lake together.
Philip slowed his own steps that they might talk.

Much of the time his father must lie down and rest.
One day he did not rise from his bed.
Philip hurried to his side
And bent low to hear his words.

"I must tell you something, my son.
For me the end is near.
Yet I have no fear.
The Lord is my shepherd . . ."

His father's voice faltered, and Philip finished the words.
"Yea, though I walk through the valley of the shadow of death,
I will fear no evil: for thou art with me;
Thy rod and thy staff they comfort me."

"I will be lonely, Father, so lonely."
Philip could not hold back the tears.
"What shall I do without you near to counsel me?
Who will answer my questions?"

His father spoke gently.
"God never fails his people, my son.
Walk in his ways each day,
And he will be to you as a loving father."

Philip saw his father's eyes close.
Again he heard his father's voice.
"Like as a father pitieth his children,
So the Lord pitieth them that fear him."

As Philip grew older, he missed his father more and more.
He was a lonely man, and a thoughtful one.
Always in his mind there was a question,
An old question that needed to be answered.

One day Philip went to the wisest man he knew.
"Tell me something," he begged.
"What is God like?"
For a long time there was silence.

Then the wise man shook his head.
"I do not know," he said.
"Canst thou by searching find out God?
Canst thou find out the Almighty?"

Years went by.
Philip spent much time alone, thinking.
He was past thirty years old
When he first heard of the carpenter from Nazareth.

The old date merchant had been down to Jerusalem.
Coming back through the Jordan valley,
He had stopped to listen to the preaching of John the Baptist.
In the market place Philip listened to the old merchant's tale.

"One day a young carpenter asked for baptism.
The preacher had not hesitated with anyone else.
This time he refused.
'I need you to baptize me,' he told the carpenter.

"The man insisted, and at last the preacher baptized him.
As he came up out of the water,
Some say that a strange thing happened." The old merchant paused.
Philip edged closer, and the story went on.

"The heavens were opened. . . .
And lo a voice from heaven, saying,
This is my beloved Son,
In whom I am well pleased."

"Who was the man?" Philip asked. "What happened then?"
"His name is Jesus," the date merchant answered.
"At first he went away. Now he is going about the country teaching.
They say people are beginning to follow him."

On the streets of Bethsaida there was news one day.
"Two of our own men have talked with the carpenter," a fisherman said.
"Andrew and Peter can speak of nothing else. Over and over they say,
'We have found . . . the Christ.' "

Philip watched and waited.
Restless, he made a trip down into the Jordan valley.
It was springtime.
Purple anemones were blooming by the roadside.

There, near Bethabarah, Jesus of Nazareth found Philip.
They talked together for a long time.
"Follow me," Jesus invited.
And the two became friends.

Philip could not keep his discovery to himself.
Under a leafy tree by the roadside,
He found his friend Nathanael looking up at the green figs.
Philip almost shouted the good news.

"We have found him!
We have found him, of whom Moses
In the law, and the prophets, did write,
Jesus of Nazareth!"

"A prophet from Nazareth?"
Nathanael repeated the words with scorn.
"Come and see," Philip begged.
And Nathanael followed him down the road to find Jesus.

Jesus welcomed Nathanael,
And Nathanael believed on him.
Wherever Jesus went,
The two men followed.

Other men joined the crowd that followed Jesus.
They listened to his words, and watched everything he did.
One day on a mountainside Philip heard Jesus calling men
For a special task. "Andrew, Peter, James, John—"

Philip held his breath, and waited.
Then he heard his own name, "Philip!"
Philip was so excited that he hardly heard the other seven names.
At last twelve men stood with Jesus.

These were the special disciples
Who would learn Jesus' work.
These were the Twelve he chose
That they should be with him,
And that he might send them forth
To preach
And to have power to heal sicknesses,
And to cast out devils.

Down the mountain Jesus led the Twelve.
The crowd followed to a level place.
People came from Jerusalem and from all Judea,
And from the sea coast towns of Tyre and Sidon.

Philip watched Jesus heal those who were sick.
He saw him bring peace to men troubled in spirit.
The people crowded close,
And Jesus helped each one of them.

More and more people came.
And the whole multitude sought to touch him:
For there went virtue out of him,
And healed them all.

Again the crowds pressed close.
Jesus went higher up the mountain,
And his disciples followed.
On a grassy slope Jesus sat down and taught them.

Philip had never heard such words,
For Jesus spoke of God and of his kingdom.
He spoke of meekness and of mercy,
And of the happy hearts of those who follow God's way.

Jesus told the way to be blessed.
Philip never forgot one thing that he said,
"Blessed are the pure in heart:
For they shall see God."

The words reminded Philip of his own old longing
To know about God and to see him.
He put Jesus' saying away in his mind
To remember and to think about.

Jesus was still talking about God.
He was calling him "my Father."
Then Philip heard something different.
Jesus said, "your Father."

Philip could hardly believe his ears.
Never had he dared think of God in that way.
Yet he counted the words twelve times
On the lips of Jesus.

Now Jesus was teaching his friends how to pray.
"After this manner therefore pray ye," he said.
And the prayer began with the words,
Our Father which art in heaven.

When the day's teaching was ended,
Philip and the other disciples followed Jesus down the mountain,
And into the town of Capernaum.
There Jesus healed a Roman captain's servant boy.

Something interesting was happening all the time.
One day Jesus and his disciples started down the road to Nain.
A great crowd followed.
Near the city gate they met a funeral procession.

With his own eyes Philip saw Jesus bring the dead man back to life.
Philip's own voice joined in the shouts of the people,
". . . A great prophet is risen up among us;
. . . God hath visited his people."

And always Jesus was healing sick people,
And comforting troubled ones.
Every day he was talking to his Heavenly Father;
Much of the time he was telling people about God.

"Jesus knows more about God than anyone else," Philip concluded.
"Maybe he can tell me what God is like."
Before Philip could ask him, Jesus said something else.
To Philip it seemed almost like a promise.

"No man knoweth . . . the Father,
Save the Son,
And he to whomsoever
The Son will reveal him."

Who was this Son of whom Jesus spoke,
The only one who knew the Father,
The one who would show him to other people?
Questions crowded into Philip's mind.

He was thinking of them one day at dinner
In the house of Simon the Pharisee.
A poor sinful woman had come weeping to Jesus.
In her hand Philip saw an alabaster box of precious perfume.

As Jesus sat at the table,
She poured the perfume on his feet.
Simon was shocked.
"Doesn't Jesus know the kind of woman this is?" he asked.

But Jesus had talked to Simon of love and mercy.
And to the woman he said,
"Thy sins are forgiven. . . .
Go in peace."

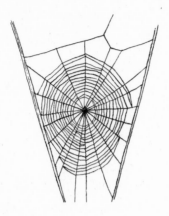

Everywhere people were talking about Jesus.
"Who is this one who forgives sin?" they muttered.
"Only God can forgive sin."
Philip thought about it.

He thought of something else too.
Jesus' words to the woman reminded Philip of an old prayer.
It was a prayer he had heard his father pray,
"Thou, Lord, art good, and ready to forgive."

Philip thought of the woman Jesus had forgiven.
Never would he forget her face—or the face of Jesus.
"Jesus must be something like God," Philip decided.
"Jesus, too, is good and ready to forgive."

Every day Philip heard Jesus preach and teach.
Every day he saw Jesus heal and help.
With the other disciples Philip went everywhere with Jesus.
He listened to catch every word Jesus said.

Philip was learning to help in Jesus' work.
At last he and the others were ready to try for themselves.
So Jesus sent out the Twelve.
He sent them out two by two.

He gave them power and authority
Over all devils, and to cure diseases.
And he sent them to preach the kingdom of God,
And to heal the sick.

Philip started down the road with Bartholomew.
Never had he been so excited.
Could they really heal sick bodies and troubled minds?
Then he remembered — it was Jesus' power they would use!

Now they had reached the first town.
By the side of the road they saw a man with twisted legs.
Philip spoke to him in the name of Jesus,
And the lame man was healed.

A crowd gathered.
And Philip healed their sick.
He preached to them,
And told them of God's love.

All over Galilee people saw wonderful things.
Blind men received their sight, and troubled minds found peace.
For the disciples of Jesus went through the towns,
Preaching the gospel, and healing everywhere.

At last the trip was over,
And twelve happy, weary men came back to Capernaum.
Down by the water,
They found Jesus.

Gathering close around him,
They told him all things,
Both what they had done,
And what they had taught.

Philip saw the proud look in Jesus' eyes,
For Jesus rejoiced in every good thing they had done.
Now his disciples were ready to learn more.
But first they must rest.

Jesus pointed to Peter's empty boat.
"Come," he said to the Twelve.
"Let's sail across the lake to a quiet place.
There we can rest a while."

Philip and the other disciples followed Jesus into the boat.
Peter untied the rope.
The wind filled the sails.
Soon the little boat was skimming across the blue water.

People standing near had heard the plan.
They started for the road that made a short cut around the lake.
When Jesus and his friends stepped from the boat,
They found a great crowd waiting.

When Jesus saw the multitude,
He felt sorry for them.
And he healed their sick
And spake unto them of the kingdom of God.

All day Jesus healed and taught.
More and more people came.
It was evening when the disciples pushed forward.
"Send these hungry people away," they told Jesus.

Jesus turned to Philip.
"Where can we buy bread for them?" he asked.
Philip shook his head.
"Just a bite for everyone would cost more than half a year's wages."

"Give the people something to eat," Jesus directed.
His disciples stared at him. Finally one spoke,
"We have only five rolls and two small fishes."
Jesus smiled. "Have the people sit down," he said.

Jesus took the food and thanked God for it.
Then he broke it and fed all the people—more than five thousand.
And the disciples gathered up twelve baskets
Of the left over fragments of bread and fish.

Philip's own eyes saw it. His own stomach was full of food.
His own hands gathered up a basket full of fragments.
Philip thought of an old prophecy about the Christ,
"His name shall be called Wonderful!"

48

The crowds went wild when they saw the miracle.
"Let's make Jesus our king!" people said one to another.
Jesus heard. Quietly he sent his disciples away in the boat.
Then he himself went to a near-by mountain to pray.

Darkness came, and with it a windstorm.
Great waves flung the little boat about in the water.
Wet and cold, the disciples strained at the oars.
It was long past midnight, and they were miles from land.

Suddenly Philip saw someone walking toward the boat.
The disciples rubbed their eyes to be sure they were not asleep.
Still they saw a man coming, walking on the water.
"It is a ghost!" they cried out in fear.

Then they heard a clear, gentle voice.
"Be of good cheer," Jesus said.
"It is I; be not afraid."
Soon he was in the boat.

The wind was still now, and the waters were quiet.
With the other disciples Philip looked at Jesus in amazement.
Then they worshiped him. Together they said,
"Of a truth thou art the Son of God."

All Capernaum had heard of the loaves and fishes.
People were urging Jesus to be their king.
"You want food for your stomachs," Jesus told them.
"I came to bring you eternal life in God.

"I am the bread of life: he that cometh to me shall never hunger;
And he that believeth on me shall never thirst."
Philip heard the words. He saw the people turn away from Jesus.
He saw too, that some of Jesus' followers went with them.

Jesus spoke of it to the Twelve one day.
"Will you also go away?" he asked.
The disciples searched for words to say what was in their hearts.
Peter found them.

"Lord, to whom shall we go?
Thou hast the words of eternal life.
And we believe and are sure that thou art that Christ,
The Son of the living God."

Again there was a trip with Jesus,
This time into the coast towns.
Philip watched Jesus give sight to blind eyes.
He saw him heal sick people and feed hungry ones.

Philip listened to everything Jesus said.
Some of the teachings were hard to understand.
One day Jesus began to talk of death.
Soon it would come to him, he said.

"The Son of man must suffer many things,
And be rejected, . . .
And be killed,
And after three days rise again."

Philip kept thinking of what Jesus said.
Alone one night he thought for a long time about it.
At last he decided something.
He must ask his question before it was too late.

Every day was a busy one.
Every day Jesus was healing and teaching.
Philip tried to find him alone, but he could not.
When would there be time for his question?

One day Jesus took three disciples up Mount Hermon with him.
At the foot of the mountain,
Philip and the others waited.
And they fretted a bit that they too could not go.

Soon they saw a crowd coming.
One man ran ahead to them. "Please make my boy well,"
He begged. "He has an evil spirit."
The disciples spoke to the boy, but nothing happened.

Even as Jesus came down the mountain, the boy grew worse.
His father hurried to Jesus.
"Your disciples could not cure my son," he explained.
"Will you heal him?"

And Jesus rebuked the unclean spirit,
And healed the child,
And delivered him again to his father.
And they were all amazed at the mighty power of God.

Philip was more puzzled than ever.
Surely Jesus could do anything!
Why didn't he use his power to get rid of his enemies?
Why must he die?

Patiently Jesus taught his disciples each day.
It was as if he had much to tell and so little time to say it.
The disciples began to hear of threats and plots in Jerusalem.
Jesus heard too, but he went up to the Passover Feast as usual.

One day in the Temple Philip heard astonishing words.
The Pharisees had been taunting Jesus.
"Who is your witness that God sent you?" they asked.
Jesus drew himself up tall and straight. Then he spoke.

"I am the light of the world . . .
The Father that sent me beareth witness of me . . .
If ye had known me,
Ye should have known my Father also."

Philip saw the anger of the Pharisees.
He saw the stones in their hands.
Before they could hurl them,
Jesus had gone away.

On a street near the Temple
Philip watched Jesus heal a man born blind.
He heard the man praise Jesus in the Temple,
And saw the Pharisees cast him out.

Jesus turned to his disciples.
He spoke of false leaders who run from danger like strange shepherds.
True leaders, he said, are like good shepherds.
Philip leaned forward to listen as Jesus went on.

"I am the good shepherd: . . .
As the father knoweth me,
Even so know I the Father:
And I lay down my life for the sheep."

Jesus' words kept singing in Philip's ears.
Along with them he remembered an old prophecy,
"Behold, the Lord God will come . . .
He shall feed his flock like a shepherd."

The short winter days passed swiftly.
Jesus was busy teaching his disciples and helping people.
Philip kept thinking about the question he wanted to ask.
He kept waiting for a time.

In the synagogue one day he saw a woman bent over almost double.
Her back had been crooked for eighteen years.
Philip watched Jesus heal the woman. He saw her stand up straight.
He heard her praise God for her healing.

He heard too the criticism of the Pharisees.
They decided to corner Jesus.
"If you are really the Christ," they said, "tell us plainly."
Philip held his breath for Jesus' answer.

"I told you, and ye believed not:
The works that I do in my Father's name,
They bear witness of me.
I and my Father are one."

Never had the Pharisees been so angry.
Philip saw them take up stones to cast them at Jesus.
Quickly he and the other disciples followed Jesus out of the city.
On the far side of the river they watched him teach and heal.

Spring flowers were blooming when Jesus and the Twelve
Started back to Jerusalem. In every village Jesus preached.
"Your enemies plot against you," friends warned. But Jesus kept on.
And all the time he was teaching his disciples.

Philip liked best the teaching about God's love for sinners.
One day Jesus told three parables of lost and found things.
One story was about a lost sheep, one was about a lost coin,
And one was about a lost boy.

Each story ended in gladness. Jesus said,
"Likewise, I say unto you,
There is joy in the presence of the angels of God
Over one sinner that repenteth."

Every moment Jesus was busy.
Yet he took time to listen to a messenger from Bethany.
"Lazarus is sick," the man said. "His sisters want you to come."
Two days passed before Jesus could go.

As Jesus and his disciples neared Bethany
Philip saw Martha weeping by the roadside.
He heard her tell of her brother's death. He saw Jesus weep with her.
Then Philip heard Jesus say an amazing thing.

"I am the resurrection, and the life:
He that believeth in me, though he were dead, yet shall he live:
And whosoever liveth and believeth in me
Shall never die."

Later, at the tomb of Lazarus,
Philip heard Jesus command the dead man to come forth.
He saw Lazarus, now four days dead,
Walk forth at Jesus' word.

News of the raising of Lazarus angered the Pharisees.
It made them even more determined to kill Jesus.
Yet Jesus went on to Jerusalem,
And his disciples went with him.

Lame and blind people, sick and troubled people,
Sorrowing and sinning people—all these crowded Jesus' path.
Philip watched him heal and help each one.
At last Jesus and his disciples reached Jerusalem.

Philip followed as Jesus rode into the city.
He saw the people waving palm branches.
He heard the crowds cheering.
Philip too joined in the song of praise.

Hosanna!
Blessed is he that cometh
In the name of the Lord! . . .
Hosanna in the highest!

In the city everything was in turmoil.
Philip heard the accusations and questioning of Jesus' enemies.
One night, with the other disciples, he ate the Passover with Jesus.
He saw Judas as he went out into the darkness to betray his master.

Then it was that Jesus gave his disciples a special supper.
They were to keep it in memory of him.
As they ate of the broken bread and drank of the cup,
They realized that Jesus would be with them for only a short time.

Jesus was comforting his disciples now.
Philip listened to his words.
"I go to prepare a place for you . . .
And whither I go ye know, and the way ye know."

Thomas it was who interrupted.
"Lord," he said,
"We do not know where you are going.
How can we know the way?"

Jesus saith unto him,
I am the way, the truth, and the life:
No man cometh unto the Father,
But by me.

Philip's question could wait no longer.
He looked straight into Jesus' eyes.
"What is God like?" he asked.
"Show us the Father."

Jesus turned to Philip.
He reached out his hand,
And laid it on Philip's shoulder.
When he spoke his voice was gentle.

"Have I been so long time with you,
And yet hast thou not known me, Philip?
He that hath seen me
Hath seen the Father."

In his mind Philip saw Jesus giving bread to hungry people.
He saw Jesus' hands stretched forth to heal the blind and the lame.
He heard Jesus speaking words of forgiveness and of blessing.
The question Philip had been asking so long was answered at last.

God is like Jesus!
Philip knew it now.
And in his heart
Philip was satisfied.

No words can ever tell all there is to know about God,
For words do not live or breathe or move.
But there is one Word that is different,
It is a living Word!

In the beginning was the Word,
And the Word was with God,
And the Word was God.
And the Word was made flesh,
And dwelt among us.
No man hath seen God at any time;
The only begotten Son, . . .
He hath declared him!

The Bible words used in this manuscript are from the King James Version, and are found as listed here:

Set in Linotype Garamond
Format by Robert Cheney
Manufactured by The Haddon Craftsmen, Inc.
Published by HARPER & BROTHERS, *New York*